THIS WALKER BOOK BELONGS TO:

_____

Fraser

_____

_____

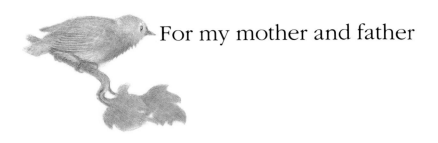

For my mother and father

First published 1992
by Walker Books Ltd, 87 Vauxhall Walk
London SE11 5HJ

This edition published 1993

© 1992 Inga Moore

Printed and bound in Hong Kong by
South China Printing Co. (1988) Ltd

British Library Cataloguing in Publication Data
A catalogue record for this book is
available from the British Library.

ISBN 0-7445-3126-8

Oh, Little Jack

Inga Moore

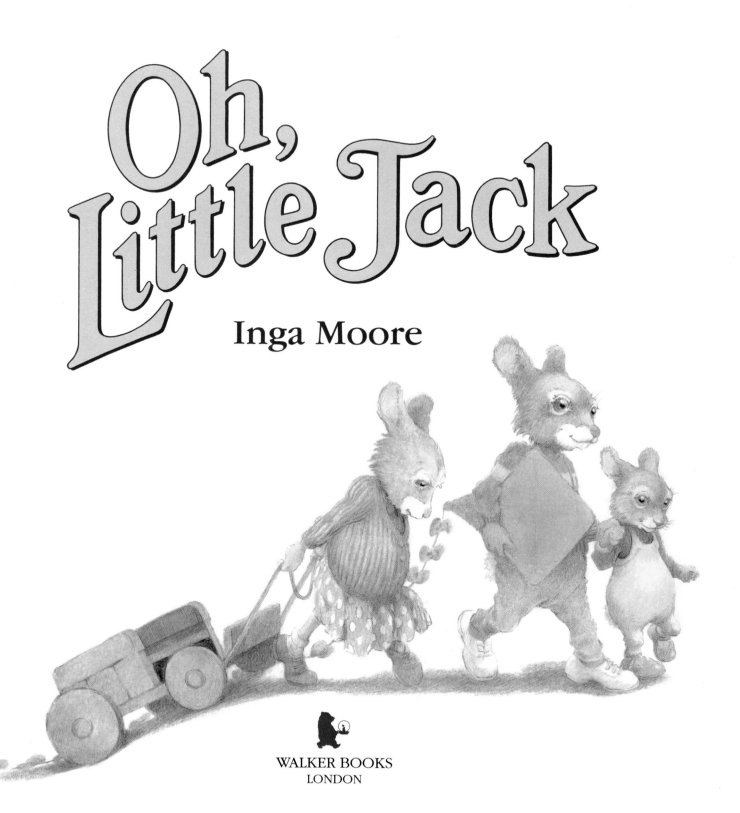

WALKER BOOKS
LONDON

It was a windy day.
Little Jack Rabbit went into the garden.

Mummy was in her vegetable patch. She was pulling
out onions.

"Can I help?" asked Little Jack.

Little Jack Rabbit found an onion with a brown curly
top. He tugged and he tugged. He tugged
as hard as he could. But he couldn't
pull it out of the ground.

"Oh, Little Jack!" said Mummy.

"I think you are too small
to pull out onions."

In the garden the wind was blowing down the leaves.
"I shall have to sweep up these leaves," said Daddy.
"Can I do it?" asked Little Jack.

Little Jack Rabbit ran to fetch the broom.
But the broom was very long.
He couldn't make it sweep.
"Oh, Little Jack!" said
Daddy. "I think you
are too small to
sweep up
leaves."

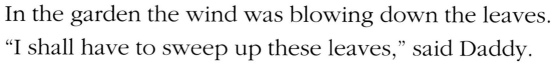

Little Jack Rabbit went to
Heathery Heath with his sister
Nancy and his big brother Buck.
Buck flew his new blue kite.
"Can I fly it?" asked Little Jack.
Little Jack Rabbit held the kite by its string.
He held it as tightly as he could. But the wind
pulled and pulled. It nearly pulled the kite away.
"Oh, Little Jack!" said Buck. "I think you
are too small to fly a kite."

On the way home Nancy rode her
billy-cart down the hill.
"Can I have a turn?" asked Little Jack.
Little Jack Rabbit sat in the billy-cart.
He rode it down the hill.
But he couldn't make
it stop at the
bottom.

"Oh, Little Jack!" said Nancy.
"I think you are too small to
ride in a billy-cart."

At home, Little Jack Rabbit went into the kitchen.
His sisters Rhona and Rita were helping Mummy
to make the tea. She was going to take some
to Granpa.
"Can I take it?" asked Little Jack.
Little Jack Rabbit picked up the cup.
He carried it as carefully as he could.
But he spilt the tea into the saucer.
"Oh, Little Jack!" said Rita.
"I think you are too small
to carry a cup of tea."

Poor Little Jack Rabbit
ran to find his granpa.
"What's the matter,
Little Jack?" Granpa asked.
"I am too small," said Little Jack.
"Too small for what?" asked Granpa.
"I am too small for everything," said Little Jack.

Granpa had been busy in his workshop.

He had been fixing something.

It was a little red tricycle.

"Who is it for?" asked Little Jack.

"It can't be for me," said Mummy.

"I am too big.

And it can't be for Daddy.

He's *much* too big."

"Is it for Buck?" asked
Little Jack.

No, the tricycle was
not for Buck. It was
not for Nancy or Rhona
or Rita. They were all too
big to ride it.

"Can I ride it?" asked Little Jack.

Little Jack Rabbit climbed on to the little
red tricycle. He was not too big
and he was not too small.
"Why, Little Jack!" said
Granpa. "You are just
the right size. The
tricycle must be
for you."
Little Jack Rabbit
rode his little red
tricycle round and
round the garden. It
was better than pulling
up onions or sweeping leaves.
It was better than flying a kite. It was
even better than riding in a billy-cart. And
it was much better than carrying a cup of tea.

"Thank you, Granpa," said Little Jack.

That night Little Jack Rabbit sat by the fire with
his family. Now he was glad he was small.
And not only because of the little red tricycle.
There was something else, something he
had forgotten. He was just the right
size to sit on Granpa's knee.

MORE WALKER PAPERBACKS
For You to Enjoy

FIFTY RED NIGHT-CAPS
by Inga Moore

This amusing, surprising and delightfully illustrated retelling of a traditional story, depicts the adventure of a boy taking a bag of night-caps to sell at the market and the troupe of playful monkeys he meets in the forest.

0-7445-1783-4   £3.99

AWAY IN A MANGER
by Sarah Hayes / Inga Moore

The Nativity story seen through the eyes of its supporting characters, with the words of six favourite carols.

"Original and informative... Rich, traditional pictures." *The Independent*

0-7445-1326-X   £3.99

THE SORCERER'S APPRENTICE
by Inga Moore

A lively version of a classic story about a meddling apprentice called Franz and the hilarious muddle he gets himself into!

"A stylish retelling... Well written and atmospherically illustrated." *The School Librarian*

0-7445-1796-6   £3.50

Walker Paperbacks are available from most booksellers, or by post from
Walker Books Ltd, PO Box 11, Falmouth, Cornwall TR10 9EN.

To order, send:
Title, author, ISBN number and price for each book ordered
Your full name and address
Cheque or postal order for the total amount, plus postage and packing:

UK and BFPO Customers – £1.00 for first book, plus 50p for the second book and plus 30p for each additional book to a maximum charge of £3.00.
Overseas and Eire Customers – £2.00 for first book, plus £1.00 for the second book and plus 50p per copy for each additional book.
Prices are correct at time of going to press, but are subject to change without notice.